Invincible Summer

A 30-DAY REFLECTIONAL ON THE POWER OF KINDNESS

Second Edition

SHERICE PERRY

Mynd Matters Publishing
715 Peachtree Street NE
Suites 100 & 200
Atlanta GA 30308

First Edition: 2018

ISBNs: 978-1-953307-93-4 (paperback); 978-1-953307-94-1 (ebook)

Printed in the United States of America

IZOLA:

You spoke light into my life when I only saw darkness.
You saw things in me I didn't see in myself. Thank you for always
reminding me that it's OK to not fit in and that I was uniquely
created by God for a reason. You're an amazing example
of the woman I hope to be.

WHAT'S INSIDE

What is a reflectional?

30 DAYS OF REFLECTION

WRAP-UP

Day 31: Reflectional recap

A NOTE FROM SHERICE

September 2021

The original intention behind this journal was – literally – a Christmas present for friends.

Never had I imagined it would go further than that – that friends of friends and even strangers – would embrace my "isms" and acts of kindness in the way they have. I consider that quite an honor.

So, first I want to say thank you for returning to *Invincible Summer*. So glad to have you back! And if it's your first time opening this reflectional, welcome to the community.

SO, WHAT THE HECK HAPPENED TO *INVINCIBLE SUMMER*?

Four months after I published *Invincible Summer*, I received a call asking me to do something I hadn't imagined I'd ever do and, in fact, had told a colleague a month earlier that I would never do: join a presidential campaign.

It wasn't in the plan. In fact, it was the furthest thing from the plan because I was just starting to settle into what I thought a "normal" life should look like. But I also believe that when you're called to serve, you should, if you have the ability to do so. Our democracy was at stake, so I jumped in.

Never. Say. Never.

WHAT'S HAPPENING NOW?

As I write this, the COVID-19 Delta variant is raging, and I'm back focusing on the work that propelled me into public service – the health and well-being of everyone in our country. COVID-19 is my day, every day. Some might say I have a habit of running to the fire, but if helping folks stay healthy and have access to the care they need is that, then I guess I'm glad old habits die hard.

So, I'm back in the game and have the awesome honor of working with one of the most brilliant women I've ever met: Dr. Marcella Nunez-Smith. She serves with integrity, keeps it authentic and is just a darn good human being. How lucky am I that I get to bust my tail working on such an important issue with someone so incredible?!

This work is far from glamorous, and I don't do it for the money; I do it because I sleep well at night knowing I've done something to improve the human condition. This pandemic has affected all of us, and in the work I do every day, I get to focus on the communities hit the hardest. I've realized that my pull to service is more than a job for me; it's a calling. I do believe my path – no matter how difficult at times – has been divinely influenced (thanks, Lisa R.). And that all has brought me to this moment. Now I see how all the other positions, big and small, prepared me for this moment. Whether it's writing a speech late at night, talking to a community-based organization about an upcoming event or pushing my colleagues to think about how our recommendations affect people who don't look like them, I feel like this is where I'm supposed to be.

Like many of you, I'm still processing what's happened since our lives came to a halt because of COVID-19. My day-to-day work revolves around the pandemic, so attempting to emotionally process it all daily would be a lot. Instead, I choose to stay focused on the goal: getting everyone vaccinated. No one is safe until we are all safe.

The thing our country can't afford not to process is that this pandemic has exposed – to a broader audience – the inequities that so many of us have known have existed for generations. People of color have been disproportionately impacted by this pandemic and have been overrepresented in COVID-19 infections, hospitalizations, and deaths.

We are finally having a public discourse about this country's history of discrimination and how that has driven policies that have left so many communities without the ability to reach their full potential. And we're finally moving toward policies that recognize – in a more holistic way – that every policy is health policy. You can't just give people insurance if there's nowhere to go for care or give them subpar care because of what they look like. And we've seen the effects of these systemic issues play out in other areas too: housing, transportation, education, employment, policing.

Dr. Nunez-Smith said it best during one of the COVID-19 Health Equity Task Force public meetings: "The year-long conversation—reckoning—following the collective witnessing of Mr. Floyd's murder should be inseparable from our shared understanding of the effects of the COVID-19 pandemic, and from our work on this Task Force. We simply cannot understand the tragedy and the toll of COVID-19—and prevent the predictability of this pattern in the future—without looking toward its drastically unequal burden on communities of color."

There's still a ton to do, but in the work I'm doing now – and the work happening all across the government – we're pushing the boundaries of what it means to have equity embedded in all policies and to examine what it means to give every person a fair shot.

ANY LESSONS YOU WANT TO SHARE FROM THE LAST FEW YEARS?

Well, of course!

FIRST, I'm working on creating **better work-life integration** this time around. Not sure "balance" exists in jobs like these, but I do know one thing – life can't be all work and no play. So, whether that's getting a massage, having drinks with friends or helping a friend babysit my crew's kiddos (with the help of wine and 80s jams), sometimes you have to disconnect and spend time with folks who know you and love you. We all need time to laugh. Time to dance around the kitchen (sliding across the floor is a must!). Time to let the brain rest.

Prior to joining the Biden campaign, I was a person who had 15 goals a year (sounds crazy now as I write that), but the campaign taught me to prioritize. I went from 15 goals to three in 2020, and one was to speak with (not text) one person a week who loved me, even if it was only for five minutes. Keeping those connections left me fuller than any meal ever could. The feeling of being loved and supported is irreplaceable.

SECOND, I realized that **I may not get what I want when I want it, but it's always on time**. I don't think it's a coincidence that I was looking for a condo around the time I was releasing this book. And for the life of me, I couldn't find a place I liked enough to commit (I'm that person who just knows "the one" when I walk into a space). And luckily, I didn't, because I had to move with the campaign and traveled quite a bit.

So, when did I finally purchase a condo? In the middle of a pandemic, while I was finishing a presidential campaign (it was a crazy time, but hey, I needed a place to live). Best part? My condo is better than anything I looked at before. It's a space that totally feels like me. I love it. I smile and say "good morning house" when I wake up. I had to leave the city, but my friends also joke that I live at a resort, so I'll take it. The wait was worth it. I'm sure you have examples of this too.

THIRD, I now know that I can be awesome on my own, or pretty good with what I call "eh" or "so-so" folks around me. But to really blow it out of the water, **I need the right people around me**. Think about how courageous you feel when you're so in love your heart leaps out of your chest or how confident you feel when you have the right boss or team around you? Often, as individuals we get used to certain situations, but that doesn't make them good for us – although hard, work on getting those right pieces in place, because that's when you'll really knock it out of the park.

AND LAST BUT CERTAINLY NOT LEAST – **I've learned to keep putting myself out there**, and I think you should try it too. Try the thing you never thought you could, the thing that scares you, the thing that looked too hard. Though not easy, I've never regretted these decisions because they reveal so much more about me than I would've ever known. I've only regretted the times I didn't try.

WHAT'S NEXT?

Ha! Not sure, but I'm here for the ride. I do know I love this reflectional and am excited to bring it back to you all.

The reality is, as this is book is getting published, we're nearing the end of 2021. The world doesn't look the same as it did when this journal was first published, and neither do we. As we work to find our new normal, I think a lot of us are recognizing that self-care isn't trendy – it's necessary.

Whether you're embarking on this 30-day journey during the summer or at the beginning of a new year in January, I hope this journal provides you with the peace and calm that this sort of quiet reflection has brought me. I hope the minutes you spend each day and with every entry fill you up with fuel to keep fighting the good fight (thanks for the reminder, Tara). And I hope this journal helps you to see and appreciate your connection with others in an even more meaningful way.

Hugs,

Shaine

> **"In the midst of winter,
> I found there was, within me,
> an invincible summer."**
>
> – ALBERT CAMUS

HEY THERE,

If you're reading this letter, you're holding my heart in your hands. So you, my friend, are pretty darn special.

We live in a fast-paced world where slowing down isn't easy or encouraged. Time for self-reflection is limited. Kindness is often overlooked and viewed as a weakness. In the midst of all the busy, it can be easy to lose perspective and forget about the things – big and small – that make our lives good. After a series of life events that left me feeling mentally drained and physically exhausted, I decided I needed a (hard) reset. That's how this book came to be.

This journal is a compilation of some of the questions I asked myself during a break I took during the summer of 2017. It's a combination of things that I've done, people I've met, conversations I've had and situations I've been in. Many of you are weaved throughout these pages.

The end result – the gift you're holding – is the reflection of some intentioned soul-searching. To figure out where I was going in life, I had to think about where I'd been and what contributions I wanted to make to this world. That required time – time to dig down deep, remember my core values and the woman I was once certain labels no longer applied. It took me a while, but I realized that if I wanted to truly be happy and leave a lasting imprint that I could be proud of, I had to drown out the noise around me and listen to my own voice. Answering these 30 questions is how I started that process.

Because I chose to slow down and embrace stillness, I learned to find calm in the storms of life. I discovered how to find joy during times of great pain. And I learned to recognize and embrace every single experience because each has made me the person that I am. This gift is patience. It's heartbreak. It's persistence. And it's restoration. It's how I found my invincible summer. This gift is me.

My faith is the grounding for who I am. It's what keeps me going (and gave me the courage to take a work break). I'm Christian, so those principles are at the foundation of the 30 questions and scriptures that are included here. But alongside each day's question for self-reflection and Bible verse is a quote that has inspired me. So, I offer this journal to anyone who wants to slow down, look inward and tune into that still, small voice.

My super-creative friend Jackie coined the term "reflectional" when I shared the idea for this journal. She said these questions are like a spiritual GPS, but instead of street-by-street directions, they are a road map to your best self. After thinking about my conversation with friends that day, it became clear to me that the journey required living in gratitude, making time for self-reflection, and being kind – to yourself and to others.

Each day's journal entry asks you to write about what you're grateful for that day and to think about a particular aspect of your life. Although not a magic bullet, I found that when things didn't seem to be going right, thinking about what I was grateful for helped to change my perspective so that I focused on what was good in my life rather than what was not. Reflecting on the person that I am helped me to stay grounded and create a vision of where I wanted to be. And the last part of each day – doing something kind for someone else – reinforced that vision by taking a concrete action to change someone else's day for the better. In a time when political divides run deep and tweets with real-world consequences dominate the daily news cycle, qualities like consideration, empathy and support of others seem even more important.

I'm not one to give directives, but my hope in sharing these questions is that you'll think about what you're thinking about – the person you are, who you hold dear, how you spend your time, the values you hold most important and your vision for your future.

The themes in this journal reflect my journey; they are self-caring and reflection, showing gratitude for others, applying lessons learned, taking steps to tackle difficult situations and thinking about the future I wanted. The thread that holds all of these together? Guidance from the still, small voice inside.

MAKING IT THROUGH WINTER

The hard part is that the noise of life can drown out that voice. For instance, I don't know whether I fully understood or had the time to completely process the trade-offs that would come with the hardest, most amazing job I've ever had. Over a number of years, I had the honor of working on the right issue – the one I'd spent my entire career working on – for the right president, at the right time. No matter how controversial or how tough, I knew every single day I was doing the right thing to help millions of people I'd never meet. I was literally living my dream to serve. Each day, I saw firsthand that even when a situation looks impossible, if you believe in what you're doing and work incredibly hard, you'll be given the grace you need to make amazing things happen.

As I watched my life play out on TV every day with the fight for affordable, high-quality health care, I was dealing with my own serious health issue. Right before I accepted my job in the Obama administration, I was diagnosed with lupus. And while working at the Department of Health and Human Services (of all places!), my kidney started to fail.

That left me with a choice to make. I could quit and try to get better or I could keep fighting. For me, being fortunate enough to have an actual choice made the only real option pretty clear. I chose to keep fighting – for myself and for the American people. Every. Single. Day.

Over the span of the first three open enrollments (and a few public health crises), I was able to travel across the country with the HHS secretary to see how our work helped children, parents, young adults and business owners pursue their dreams. Juggling a job that routinely required getting up at 4 a.m. for morning television interviews usually didn't work well for the fatigue, inflammation and joint pain that comes with lupus. But having good doctors and access to the medication I needed throughout the various stages of my illness helped push me out of bed every day. I was getting to fulfill my potential, and I wanted every single person across the country to have that same opportunity.

Like many of my colleagues, my time with friends and family became extremely limited. I missed weddings, birthdays and vacations. The open enrollment period started before Thanksgiving and ended after my birthday in early February, so the holiday season wasn't necessarily one of rest and rejuvenation. This is when I became a card sender. I could write a note at midnight or between meetings during the day. Finding time to consistently call friends and family at a decent hour was a lot harder.

But I never regretted that decision. Not one bit. I was working toward a goal that so was much greater than anything I was sacrificing in that moment.

It's crazy how facing your own mortality will give you perspective. You start to look at things a lot differently because your time could be limited. In the midst of all of this, I also went through a divorce.

The thing is – even when it's the right decision, divorce is one of the hardest things a person can go through. It's a very lonely experience, one that truly shows you who has your back. Holidays are different; your bank account looks different; your vision for the future must look different. When there's no safety net and the support you expected to be there isn't, it can be incredibly hurtful.

But surprisingly, you can also discover people's amazingly supportive and thoughtful sides that you may never have seen except in this horrible circumstance. That's the type of support that helps you to course correct and move forward into your destiny.

Even though all of these situations (and others – it was a crazy few years!) were incredibly difficult, they all brought me to this moment and to a place where I can share these words with you: I survived. I made it through winter. I'm still warming up, but let me tell you, it feels good to have the sun on my face again. And through it all, I learned a whole heck of a lot about how I value myself – and other people – in the process.

My Invincible Summer

Here are some of the other things I realized during those summer months off:

ACCEPTING MYSELF, FLAWS AND ALL

Life isn't perfect, but I love it anyway. I genuinely like the person I am now. I really do. I smile more. I'm comfortable in my own skin. I say what I think. The leap of faith I took with my career, although scary, was one of the best things I could've ever done, because not only did I find a new job – I found one that still allows me to serve by working to help communities across the country communicate about the change they want to see. I still love a good basketball game, potatoes with my meat and sending people cards to let them know I'm thinking of them. I'd like to say I'm Zen all the time, but my email is still out of control and there's probably going to be at least one person who still gets on my nerves. And I still make mistakes – but now, I don't let the mistakes make me. I'm me, and that's just fine.

BEING KIND TO OTHERS

Kindness (genuine kindness) attracts kindness. And the best way to get through a tough time is to remember what you're grateful for and to make a conscious effort to help someone else.

SETTING BOUNDRIES

I've stopped pleasing others to the detriment of myself. I realized that questioning the authority figures in my life isn't a bad thing. I learned that hurt and insecure people hurt other people (but so do mean-spirited people). I learned that disrespect, no matter how "well-intentioned" (whatever that means?!), is still disrespect and that things don't get better until people truly own their stuff.

STANDING UP FOR MYSELF

Standing up for myself doesn't make me disrespectful to others – it means I value myself enough not to let people walk all over me. And I do things now because I really want to and not because I'm being guilted into it. Fear shouldn't be the motivator in any relationship or situation; realizing the dream should be.

SHOOTING FOR EXCELLENCE ALL AROUND (BECAUSE SUBPAR JUST ISN'T WHO I AM)

"OK" isn't good enough, when "amazing" is possible, especially in relationships (I mean, if "OK" were never good enough at work, why should it be in my personal life?). Sometimes you have to be your biggest cheerleader, because you may never win approval or support from those you want it from the most. And that is OK. Sometimes the people in your life can't give you what they never had. It sucks. But you learn to cheer on yourself. You teach yourself things you didn't see elsewhere. And when you need it, the right folks appear to help you along the way.

EMBRACING HOW GOD UNIQUELY MADE ME

My sensitivity and ability to feel things deeply helps me connect with people. It fuels my desire to use my life's work to level the playing field for everyday folks. It took a while for me to own that and to realize that anyone who tries to use that character trait against me isn't anyone I should spend time around. No, thank you. I now choose to be around people who believe in me, embrace my uniqueness and make me want to be the best version of me.

BEING REALLY HONEST ABOUT WHAT I WANT

True love makes you feel like you can conquer the world, and you should fight for that. Really fight for it. You should cherish it, because so many people never get to experience real soul intimacy in the first place. It exists. And there's nothing like it in the world.

REFUSING TO GIVE UP

When things look at their absolute worst, you're stronger than you think you are. If you hang on just one more day, things can and will get better. The universe honors that.

I hope this 30-day journey leaves you feeling grateful for each day that you have on this earth. I hope you (literally!) stop and smell the roses. I hope you live more fully in the moment and embrace your inner awesomeness. I hope you celebrate the blessings in your everyday life and the people who bring them to you. And most of all, I hope it helps bring you closer to the person you are meant to be.

I'm still on this earth because there is something for me to accomplish. And I think that applies to you too. We get one life to live, and this is it. You might as well ride this bike until the wheels fall off.

May this year bring you excellent health, tons of laughter, moments you'll never forget and dreams come true.

Love,

Sherie

> What counts in life is not the mere fact that you lived. It is what difference we have made to the lives of others that will determine the significance of the life we lead.

— NELSON MANDELA

What is a reflectional?

Reflectional = +

REFLECTION   **DEVOTIONAL**

Where self-reflection, kindness
and spirituality meet.

You've heard my story.

Now it's time to write about yours.

Whether it's smooth sailing or a hot mess, take a moment to write a few lines about where you are and what made you want to invest in this kind of self-reflection for 30 days. **What do you hope to gain?**

Is there something you'd like to learn?
Keep that in mind this month.

*When doubts filled
my mind, your
comfort gave me
renewed hope
and cheer.*

PSALM 94:19 NLT

TO FEEL, GOOD, DO GOOD

— DEBASISH MRIDHA

Three things I'm grateful for today:

1.

2.

3.

When do you feel at your best?

Is there someone you know who isn't feeling at their best?

Is there something you can do to help this individual
remember their awesomeness? **Great, now go do it.**

ENCOURAGEMENT

Three things I'm grateful for today:

1.

2.

3.

What do you like most about yourself? Consider copying the compliment in a place you see often so that when you need a boost, you'll have instant encouragement in front of you.

Who could use your encouragement today?
Find something you like about someone else and tell that individual.

TO LOVE

ONESELF

IS THE

BEGINNING

OF A

LIFELONG

Romance

— OSCAR WILDE

And so encourage one another and help another, just as you are now doing.

1 THESSALONIANS 5:11 GNT

When you recover or discover something that nourishes your soul and brings joy, care enough about yourself to make room for it in your life.

— JEAN SHINODA BOLEN

Beloved, I pray that in all respects you may prosper and be in good health, just as your soul prospers.

3 JOHN 1:2 NASB

Three things I'm grateful for today:

1.

2.

3.

What gives you fuel and feeds your soul?

Are you giving yourself enough time to fill up? If not, are there changes you can make to ensure you're not running on empty? **Remember, you can't be good to anyone else if you're not taking care of yourself.**

Take a look and your schedule and see when you can set aside some **"me time."**

7

STRENGTH & COURAGE | Date:

STRENGTH & COURAGE

Three things I'm grateful for today:

1.

2.

3.

What gives you strength? What gives you courage?

Take a minute to think about how you can help instill
strength or courage in someone else. **Now do it!**

Being deeply loved by someone

GIVES YOU STRENGTH,

while loving someone deeply

GIVES YOU

courage.

Be strong and courageous. Do not fear or be in dread of them, for it is the LORD your God who goes with you. He will not leave you or forsake you.

DEUTERONOMY 31:6 ESV

YOUR DREAMS

IT ALWAYS SEEMS IMPOSSIBLE UNTIL IT'S DONE.

— NELSON MANDELA

For nothing is impossible with God.

LUKE 1:37 ESV

Three things I'm grateful for today:

1.

2.

3.

Is there a dream in your heart that seems impossible? **Write about it here.**

Do you know someone with an "impossible" dream?
End with a short prayer of encouragement for both of you.

JOY

Three things I'm grateful for today:

1.

2.

3.

Who or what makes you smile from deep down inside?

If it's who, tell that individual. Send a note or text. Hopefully that puts a smile on their face! **If it's what, set aside time to do that activity.** Consider inviting someone to join you.

SURROUND YOURSELF WITH PEOPLE WHO MAKE YOU HAPPY.

People who make you laugh, people who help you when you're in need.

PEOPLE WHO GENUINELY *care.*

—KARL MARX

The Spirit of God has made me, and the breath of the Almighty gives me life. **JOB 33:4 ESV**

Give, and it will be given to you.
A good measure, pressed down,
shaken together and running
over, will be poured into your lap.
For with the measure you use, it
will be measured to you.

LUKE 6:38 NIV

For it is in giving that we receive

—ST. FRANCIS OF ASSISI

Three things I'm grateful for today:

1.

2.

3.

It is said that whatever you need, you should give to others and the universe will bring it back to you. If you need kindness, show others kindness. If you need friendship, be a good friend.

What could you use more of today?
In what ways can you give what you need to others?

After you've thought about it, pick one thing you could use more of in your life. **Try to give more of it to others this week.**

INSPIRATION | Date:

INSPIRATION

Three things I'm grateful for today:

1.

2.

3.

What's your favorite Bible scripture or inspirational quote?

Why does this particular verse/quote speak to you?

Send it to someone and say a brief prayer for that person.

Nothing splendid has ever been achieved except by those who dared believe that something inside them was superior to circumstance.

— BRUCE BARTON

For I know the plans I have for you," declares the LORD, "plans to prosper you and not to harm you, plans to give you hope and a future."

JEREMIAH 29:11 NIV

The one who blesses others is abundantly blessed; those who help others are helped.

PROVERBS 11:25 MSG

I expect to pass through life but once. If therefore, there be any kindness I can show, or any good thing I can do to any fellow being, let me do it now, and not defer or neglect it, as I shall not pass this way again.

— **WILLIAM PENN**

Three things I'm grateful for today:

1.

2.

3.

Who was a blessing to you this week? How?

Is there something you can do to be a blessing to someone else today? (Anyone counts, whether you know the individual or not.)
Commit to being a blessing today.

YOUR SONG

Three things I'm grateful for today:

1.

2.

3.

What's your favorite song? **Play it.**
What comes to mind when you hear it?
What feeling does the song evoke that you want to hold on to?

Send the song to someone you love.
Let the person know it's dedicated to them today.

MUSIC IS THE UNIVERSAL LANGUAGE OF MANKIND.

— HENRY WADSWORTH LONGFELLOW

Three things in human

life are important:

the first is to be kind;

the second is to be kind;

and the third is to

BE
KIND.

— HENRY JAMES

*Let your speech always be gracious, seasoned
with salt, so that you may know how you
ought to answer everyone.*

COLOSSIANS 4:6 ESV

Three things I'm grateful for today:

1.

2.

3.

Kindness is a character trait that is often underrated and under appreciated. Take a few minutes to think about the people in your life. Who is the kindest person you know?

What have you observed from this person's life that you can apply to your life? **Write about it here.**

How can you show kindness to the kindest person you know?
Think about how and do it.

LOVE

Three things I'm grateful for today:

1.

2.

3.

Write a (short!) love letter to someone in your life. Tell that person why they mean so much to you.

Love is patient, love is kind. It does not envy, it does not boast, it is not proud. It does not dishonor others, it is not self-seeking, it is not easily angered, it keeps no record of wrongs. Love does not delight in evil but rejoices with the truth. It always protects, always trusts, always hopes, always perseveres. Love never fails. But where there are prophecies, they will cease; where there are tongues, they will be stilled; where there is knowledge, it will pass away.

1 CORINTHIANS
13:4–8 NIV

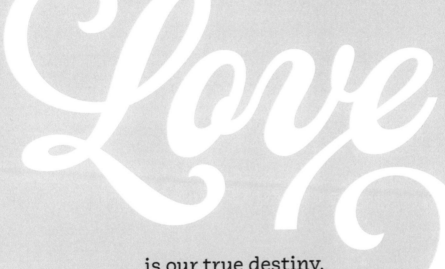

is our true destiny.

We do not find the meaning

of life by ourselves alone.

We find it with another.

— THOMAS MERTON

She is clothed with strength and dignity, and she laughs without fear of the future. When she speaks, her words are wise, and she gives instructions with kindness. She carefully watches everything in her household and suffers nothing from laziness. Charm is deceptive, and beauty does not last; but a woman who fears the LORD will be greatly praised. Reward her for all she has done. Let her deeds publicly declare her praise.

PROVERBS 31:25–27; 30–31 NLT

Blessed is he who has learned to admire but not envy, to follow but not imitate, to praise but not flatter, and to lead but not manipulate.

— THOMAS MERTON

Three things I'm grateful for today:

1.

2.

3.

Who (currently in your life) do you most admire? Why?

Consider expressing your admiration
in a note, via text or by phone.

UNCONDITIONAL SUPPORT

Three things I'm grateful for today:

1.

2.

3.

Who believes in you when it seems that no one else does? **Take a few minutes to write a short note to that person to express what their support has meant to you.**

Are you this person for someone else? If so, for whom?
If not, who can you begin to show unconditional support to?

  Commit to supporting someone today.

Surround yourself with the dreamers and the doers, the believers and thinkers, but most of all, surround yourself with those who see the

greatness within you,

even when you don't see it yourself.

— EDMUND LEE

Carry each other's burdens, and in this way you will fulfill the law of Christ.

GALATIANS 6:2 NIV

There is something in every one of you that waits and listens for the sound of the genuine in yourself. It is the only true guide you will ever have.

— HOWARD THURMAN

Be strong and courageous. Do not fear or be in dread of them, for it is the LORD your God who goes with you. He will not leave you or forsake you.

DEUTERONOMY 31:6 ESV

Three things I'm grateful for today:

1.

2.

3.

Have you ever gone against the grain and listened to that small, still voice inside instead of the loud voices around you? What did that teach you?

What is that voice saying to you today? Is there something you can do to tune into that voice a bit more? How can you act on what you're hearing? Write here how you plan to do that.

Consider sharing your plan with someone you trust.

FACING A CHALLENGE

Three things I'm grateful for today:

1.

2.

3.

Are you facing a challenge that's beginning to wear on you?
Tell God what's on your heart.

Is there someone you know who is also facing a challenge?
Ask God if there is something you can do to lighten that person's load.

Send that person a quick text with **words of encouragement.**

*Anxious hearts
are very heavy,
but a word of
encouragement
does wonders!*

PROVERBS 12:2 TLB

NO
PRESSURE
NO
DIAMONDS

— THOMAS CARLYLE

The purpose of life is to discover your gift. The work of life is to develop it. The meaning of life is to give your gift away.

— DAVID VISCOTT

As each has received a gift, use it to serve one another, as good stewards of God's varied grace.

1 PETER 4:10 ESV

Three things I'm grateful for today:

1.

2.

3.

God made all of us in a special, distinct way. Each person has been given unique gifts. What gifts has God given you? Are you fully utilizing them?

What more can you do to hone your gifts and share them with others?

Commit to doing one thing to hone and share your gift (there's nothing too big or too small).

CRUSHING IT

Three things I'm grateful for today:

1.

2.

3.

Write about the last time you felt like you crushed it.
How did it make you feel?

Is there something you learned from that experience that you can
apply to a situation that is more challenging right now?

Is there someone in your life who is crushing it? **Tell them.**

When you are inspired

by some great purpose,

some extraordinary

project, all your thoughts

break *their* bounds.

Let your light so
shine before men,
that they may see
your good works,
and glorify your
Father which
is in heaven.

MATTHEW 5:16 KJV

To forgive is to set a prisoner free and discover that the prisoner was you.

— LEWIS B. SMEDES

*Instead, be kind to each
other, tenderhearted, forgiving
one another, just as God through
Christ has forgiven you.*

EPHESIANS 4:32 NLT

Three things I'm grateful for today:

1.

2.

3.

Write about a time someone forgave you. How did it make you feel? What did you learn from that experience?

Is there someone you need to forgive right now?
Is that person you?

Find a quiet spot. Take five minutes and think about one step you can take towards showing yourself, or someone else, forgiveness.

FOCUS ON THE GOOD

Three things I'm grateful for today:

1.

2.

3.

The Bible tells us that God uses everything for our good. Everything includes everything, even the bad stuff ... like bad situations and the things we don't always like about ourselves. Has there been a circumstance in your life that seemed all bad but good came from it? What did that situation teach you about yourself?

Is there someone you know who could use reassurance that God can make good from something that seems bad? **Reach out and remind that individual.**

There is a crack in everything.

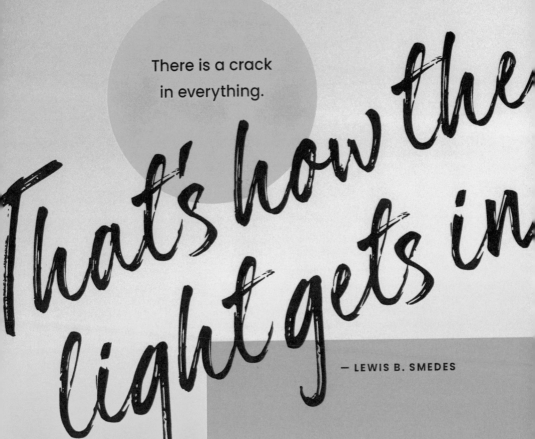

That's how the light gets in

— LEWIS B. SMEDES

Instead, be kind to each other, tenderhearted, forgiving one another, just as God through Christ has forgiven you.

EPHESIAN 4:32 NLT

41

Do all the good you can, by all the means you can,

in all the ways you can, in all the places you can,

at all the times you can, to all the people you can,

as long as ever

YOU CAN

— JOHN WESLEY

Blessed are those who find wisdom, those who gain understanding,
for she is more profitable than silver and yields better returns than gold.
She is more precious than rubies; nothing you desire can compare
with her. Long life is in her right hand; in her left hand are riches
and honor. Her ways are pleasant ways, and all her paths are peace.
She is a tree of life to those who take hold of her;
those who hold her fast will be blessed.

PROVERBS 3:13–18 NIV

Three things I'm grateful for today:

1.

2.

3.

What's the best piece of advice you've ever received?
How did it help you?

Is there someone you think could use this advice today?
If so, share it.

PROGRESS

Three things I'm grateful for today:

1.

2.

3.

Have you been making progress toward a big goal or tackling a big problem? Awesome! Reflect on the effort you've put in and how that's made you feel.

What can you do to celebrate your progress?

Is there someone who has been supporting you along the way? **If so, reach out to express your gratitude.**

The man who moves a mountain begins by carrying away small stones.

— CONFUCIUS

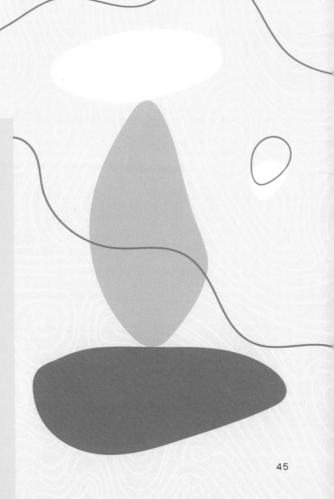

Brothers and sisters, I do not consider myself yet to have taken hold of it. But one thing I do: Forgetting what is behind and straining toward what is ahead, I press on toward the goal to win the prize for which God has called me heavenward in Christ Jesus.

PHILIPPIANS 3:13-14 NIV

Twenty years from now you will be more disappointed by the things you didn't do than by the ones you did do. So throw off the bowlines. Sail away from the safe harbor. Catch the trade winds in your sails.

EXPLORE
Dream
Discover

— MARK TWAIN

The LORD himself will lead you and be with you. He will not fail you or abandon you, so do not lose courage or be afraid.

DEUTERONOMY 31:8 GNT

Three things I'm grateful for today:

1.

2.

3.

What is one thing would you do if you weren't afraid?

Is there one small step you can take today to get closer to trying it?
Do you have anything to lose?

Is there someone in your life — a child, a friend or family member
— who is letting fear stop them from pursuing something
worthwhile? **Share a word of encouragement today.**

GOALS

Three things I'm grateful for today:

1.

2.

3.

If you could accomplish one key thing in one area of your life, what would it be?

What's one thing you can do this month to bring you closer to that goal?

How about next month? Two months from now?

For the rest of the year? **Commit to taking the first step today.**

I don't care how much power, brilliance or energy you have,

if you don't harness it and

FOCUS

it on a specific target, and hold it there you're never

going to accomplish as much as your ability warrants.

— ZIG ZIGLAR

JUSTICE

I hope that my achievements in
life shall be these – that I will have
fought for what was right and fair, that
I will have risked for that which mattered,
and that I will have given help to those
who were in need that I will have
left the earth a better place for what
I've done and who I've been.

— CARL HOPPE

*Speak up for those
who cannot speak
for themselves, for
the rights of all
who are destitute.*

**PROVERBS
31:8 NIV**

Three things I'm grateful for today:

1.

2.

3.

Is there an injustice in the world that really angers you? **Write about it here.**

What can you do today – big or small – to help make our society a more equitable place for everyone?

Commit to taking action.

YOUR WORDS | Date:

YOUR WORDS

Three things I'm grateful for today:

1.

2.

3.

Is there something you said recently that you wish you hadn't?
Why'd you feel that way?

If your words damaged a relationship, is there something you
can do to begin to smooth things over? **Take that first step today.**

Be careful with your words. Once they are said, they can only be forgiven, not forgotten.

— UNKNOWN

Let your speech always be gracious, seasoned with salt, so that you may know how you ought to answer everyone.

COLOSSIANS 4:6 ESV

Friends come and friends go, but a true friend sticks by you like family.

PROVERBS 18:24 MSG

Friendship is the source of the greatest pleasure, and without friends even the most agreeable pursuits become tedius.

— ST. THOMAS AQUINAS

Three things I'm grateful for today:

1.

2.

3.

Is there a friend you haven't spoken to in a while who you would like to reconnect with?

What do you miss most about them?

Reach out to your friend and **share that they are in your thoughts**.

YOUR THOUGHTS

Three things I'm grateful for today:

1.

2.

3.

It's often said that if you want to know what your future looks like, ask yourself what you're thinking about today. Based on your thoughts, what are you on track to become? Is it exciting? Is it scary? Does it make you smile, or does it make you sigh?

Who in your life needs a reminder about the importance of their thought life? **Reach out with some encouraging words.**

CHANGE YOUR THOUGHTS

AND
YOU

change
your
world.

— NORMAN VINCENT PEALE

Be careful what you think,
because your thoughts run your life.

PROVERBS 4:23 NCV

In the end, it's not the

years in your life that count.

It's the life in your years

— ADLAI
STEVENSON

*You make known to
me the path of life; in
your presence there
is fullness of joy; at
your right hand are
pleasures forevermore.*

PSALM 16:11 ESV

Three things I'm grateful for today:

1.

2.

3.

What advice would you give your 17-year-old self?

What do you want to be able to say about your 70-year-old self?

Is there something you need to begin doing so the things
you say to your 70-year-old self will turn out to be true?
Commit to taking one action step today.

YOUR MESSAGE

Three things I'm grateful for today:

1.

2.

3.

What message do you want people to receive from your life?

How can you walk more fully in your "message" today?

How can you encourage someone else to do the same?

Give it a try.

MY LIFE IS MY MESSAGE

— MAHATMA GANDHI

Let your light so shine before men, that they may see your good works, and glorify your Father which is in heaven.

MATTHEW 5:16 KJV

Invincible Summer

30-DAY RECAP

Congrats, you made it! I hope you've experienced a breakthrough (or two) during these last 30 days of introspection and that those discoveries have helped you pave a new path forward. As you continue to build on the journey you've taken, you may stumble, but come back and look at the notes you've written here. Your honesty, courage and thoughtfulness will help keep you focused. When you've made considerable progress, open this up and remind yourself of where you've been and all that you have accomplished.

Applaud yourself for the steps you have taken
and use it as motivation to keep going.

What have the last 30 days been like for you?
Did you make any surprising discoveries?

Which day's question was the easiest to answer? Why?

Which day's question was the hardest to answer? Why?

How were your acts of kindness received?

Do you think you'll continue to do some of these things?

ACKNOWLEDGMENTS

I never would have created this journal without the support of these very special people:

The *Invincible Summer* Team:

JOY – Your support during this journey has been nothing short of extraordinary. You will always be more than a copyeditor to me. Trusting you with my words made you a friend.

NEECHIE – Your enthusiasm and encouragement for this project from the very beginning has meant so much to me. Your counsel made you a partner, but your care keeps you close to my heart.

BRIDGET – Thank you for joining the *Invincible Summer* family and for helping to bring my dream back to life. Your beautiful work is a true reflection of what this journal was always meant to be.

The folks who supported this book getting to the finish line:

ANDY – You listened when this was just an idea and told me to write. And you gave me my first real shot at what would become my life's work. I will always be grateful to you.

NATE F, STEFANIE, DANIEL, DAMION, LENNY, LYNDA, ANDREA, GERALDINE, STEPHANIE, KIRBY, KILARA, MAYRA, TAMIA, MARIA, ALEX, SONJA, LAUREN, ANGELA G., KAEN, CIDES, MIKE, TOREY, SANDY, DANI, DAMON, SEF, NEDEEKA and friends past and present who encouraged me in this process – thank you for your support while this idea evolved.

CANDICE – Thank you for your support of this project at every step. I'm grateful that you're my sister. I love that you're my friend.

BRE – Though there are a lot of years between us, you've taught me a lot. I love you and look forward to continuing to learn from you sissy.

LISA – Thank you for explaining the beauty of "bashert" to me and for suggesting I share my story in the introduction.

ELLIE, KARA AND JACKIE – Your enthusiasm for this project gave it new life after it had been sitting on the shelf. I'm forever grateful. And Jackie – your insanely creative brain spurred the whole conversation that got us to the title. Thank you for encouraging me to share my words with the world.

To the most awesome group of guinea pigs a girl could've ever asked for: **KARA, PRITA, JEN, PRISCILLA, MAYRA, MARQUES AND SABRINA** – thank you for reinforcing the hope I had for this project. Thank you for giving me a glimpse into your lives and, most importantly, your hearts.

DAVID – You're incredibly talented. Thank you for making me sound so cool.

STEPHEN – Your counsel was invaluable to a girl who just wanted to work on a Christmas gift for friends. Thank you for being so generous with your time. Your "blessing" means a lot to me.

DORI – The opportunity you gave me opened up a world I never knew existed. Not only did you show me government could *look good* but that you really could *do good*. I appreciate you and your mentorship.

KRISTEN – I will always carry the memory of *Invincible Summer's* debut because of you. Thank you for believing in this project and for showing me that entrepreneurship is possible.

The incredible principals I've worked for:

You're the incredible women I've had the honor to support during my professional career: **KATHLEEN SEBELIUS, SYLVIA MATHEWS BURWELL, BILLIE JEAN KING** and **DR. JILL BIDEN**. Thank you for everything you taught me. Whether I watched you go to battle for health care, campaign to help save our democracy, advocate to level the playing field in sports or work to diversify the C-suite, you all had one thing in common – your desire to provide everyone with an opportunity to reach their full potential. Your intellect, grace, grit and sense of style have inspired me. Thank you for being a part of my life.

DR. MARCELLA NUNEZ-SMITH – There is no one I would've rather gone into the COVID-19 battle with than you. You're brilliant. And a wonderful human being. I will always appreciate you and your presence in my life. You inspire me every day. And **TARA** – I would've never been able to support **MNS** without you. So glad to call you a friend now.

And last but certainly not least – my amazing doctors:

JUSTIN AND JAGDEEP – I could not have asked for better doctors. Not only did you give me great care, but you listened to what I wanted and worked with me despite my challenging life and schedule, not just during my time in the Obama Administration, but the 20 months I spent on the Biden campaign. There's no thank you that will ever suffice for keeping me on this earth long enough to write (and re-release) this reflectional. I'm eternally grateful to you both.

ABOUT
THE TEAM

SHERICE PERRY

After fast-paced years working in health care policy in the Obama administration, it was only when Sherice Perry slowed down that she finally achieved an elusive goal: renewal and rediscovery.

For Sherice, working at the Department of Health and Human Services on health care wasn't just a dream job – it was a journey of a lifetime. Her own lupus diagnosis underscored just how much millions of Americans depended on affordable, reliable care, especially the low-income families, women and communities of color for whom she had spent over a decade as an advocate.

By summer 2017, Sherice arrived at a realization dramatically different from most Washingtonians in a hurry: She needed to hit pause for the sake of her own health – physically, mentally and spiritually. Over the summer months, journaling became Sherice's gateway to self-reflection. Putting pen to paper restored her confidence in herself and helped her regain a vision for her future. In this 30-day reflectional, Sherice lays out the path she took on this journey of rediscovery in the hopes that others can navigate their own way forward.

A native New Yorker and graduate of the University of Pennsylvania, Sherice holds a master's degree in public policy from Georgetown University and studied at Oxford University. Today, she is serving in the Biden-Harris administration focusing on equity in the COVID-19 pandemic response. Recognizing the influence youth sports has on her life, Sherice also loves delving into projects that explore the power of sport to change individuals, communities and society.

INVINCIBLE SUMMER: A 30-DAY REFLECTIONAL ON THE POWER OF KINDNESS IS SHERICE'S FIRST BOOK.

Neechie Greer is a DC-based digital guru who specializes in building software and technical solutions to make the world a better place. A former health and fitness professional, Neechie is a graduate of Howard University whom you can catch dancing to her own beat, literally, or participating in competitive sports (especially flag football) when she isn't in her lair. Connect with Neechie at **findyourneechie.com** to learn more about her current projects.

Bridget Letchos is a graphic and UX designer based in Forest Park, IL. A mom of two crazy, tea-drinking littles, Bridget is a hopeless optimistic who loves all things Taco Bell and will always be a Disney kid at heart. Check out Bridget and her work at **bletchos.com**.

Joy Metcalf is a DC-based editor with almost 20 years of experience editing all types of publications and media. She is a graduate of Franklin & Marshall College. She lives in Northern Virginia with her husband and daughter and is a true Chipotle lover. You can find out more about Joy at **stetediting.com**.

CPSIA information can be obtained
at www.ICGtesting.com
Printed in the USA
BVRC092340061221
623316BV00017B/1

Ring of FIRE

by Barbara Fierman

PEARSON
Scott
Foresman

What You Already Know

The outermost layer of Earth is the crust. The thickness of the crust varies—areas covered by oceans are about five kilometers thick, while areas of dry land can be thirty kilometers thick. The layer below the crust is the mantle. The outer part of the mantle, like the crust, is solid. The inner part is extremely hot, so hot that the rock is partially melted.

The innermost layer of Earth is the core. The core is quite dense as a result of the pressure of the rock above it. The temperature of the core is about 5,000°C, just about the same as that of the Sun.

The crust and the solid part of the mantle make up the lithosphere. The lithosphere is broken into pieces called tectonic plates. These plates are of different shapes and sizes. Most of the lithosphere is actually under the oceans and other bodies of water on Earth.

molten core

mantle

This model shows a slice through the Earth.

oceanic crust

continental crust

lithosphere

In the early 1900s, a German scientist named Alfred Wegener proposed a theory to explain the movement of the plates. His theory, known as continental drift, states that the continents drifted apart in the past, and still continue to do so. Several pieces of evidence support this theory. However, Wegener couldn't account for the force that caused the movement.

Wegener's theory also failed to explain many features of the Earth's crust. Currently, scientists rely on the theory of plate tectonics to explain the appearance of Earth's features. According to this theory, Earth's lithosphere is composed of about twenty plates floating on a layer of partly melted rock. The theory also explains many of Earth's features, such as how continents break apart, how mountain chains form, how volcanoes erupt, or how oceans change size.

The areas where two plates meet are referred to as plate boundaries. When plates move toward each other, they can rise up and form mountains. When one plate slides below another, faults, or breaks in Earth's crust, may form. This type of movement can cause earthquakes.

Volcanic Regions

Most volcanoes of the world are found along the boundaries of major plates. The origin of volcanoes is closely related to the movement of Earth's plates. Earthquakes are vibrations, sometimes very violent, that follow a release of energy in the Earth's crust. They also occur on or near plate boundaries.

If you plotted the locations of volcanic activity on a map, you would see that most of them form a rim around the Pacific Ocean. Actually, about 80 percent of the world's earthquakes have occurred along this rim. More than 75 percent of the world's volcanoes are located along the rim. Because of the extensive volcanic and earthquake activity, the area has become known as the Ring of Fire.

You can use the map key to identify the Ring of Fire on the map of volcanic regions shown below. Follow the Ring of Fire as it stretches from New Zealand north through Indonesia, the Philippines, and Japan; continues through eastern Russia and east along the Aleutian Islands of Alaska; and then continues south along the western coasts of North and South America. Notice the number of volcanoes located along the Ring of Fire. These volcanoes are located on the boundaries, or edges, of the Pacific plate.

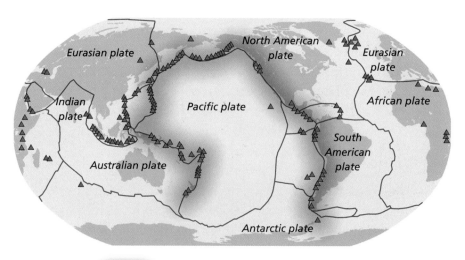

Map Key: ⬜ Ring of Fire —— plate boundary ▲ volcano

Cerro Negro, a volcano in northern Nicaragua, has erupted at least twenty times since 1850.

Moving Plates

Earth's crust is cracked into about twenty pieces called tectonic plates. Tectonic plates can be classified as continental or oceanic plates. Continental plates are located mainly under continents, and oceanic plates are located mainly under the ocean. Scientists estimate that the plates range from twenty-five to sixty miles in thickness.

Earth's crust is split into sections called tectonic plates.

Tectonic plates are like rafts of solid rock that float on the mantle beneath them. As the mantle moves, the tectonic plates move too. The moving plates pull away from, collide with, or scrape past each other. Although the plates move very, very slowly, the power of their collisions is great.

When two plates collide, the lighter plate is often forced up over the heavier one. This action can cause cracks in the mantle. Eventually, these cracks create openings that allow molten, or melted, rock to rise up out of Earth's core.

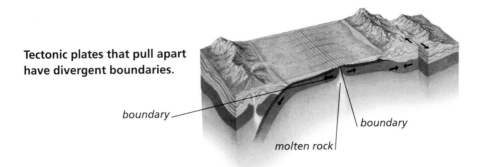

Tectonic plates that pull apart have divergent boundaries.

boundary

boundary

molten rock

The action of tectonic plates results in different types of boundaries between them. Divergent boundaries, such as those of the Mid-Atlantic Ridge, separate from each other. When the plates pull apart, magma, or molten rock, comes up from Earth's inner layers to form a new crust. Convergent boundaries form when two plates meet in a collision, or one slides over the other. Transform fault boundaries form when plates slide along one another. Most volcanoes and earthquakes occur because of the activity at plate boundaries.

Indonesia is located at the boundary of several plates. As a result, more than 125 active volcanoes exist there. An example is Merapi, on the island of Java. Merapi is the most active composite volcano in Indonesia. It has erupted at least sixty-eight times since 1548.

The mountain in the center is Mt. Bromo, one of over 125 active volcanoes in Indonesia.

Why do plates move? Scientists have proposed different explanations to answer the question. One explanation is the convection cell theory. It states that streams of magma are pushed upward from deep within Earth and out onto the ocean floor. As the molten rock cools and hardens, it forms new rock and causes the ocean floor to spread. This process pushes the plates.

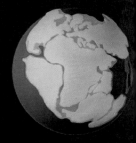

220 million years ago

Another explanation is the plume theory. This theory states that plumes, or huge balls of extremely hot rock, exist in the lower part of the mantle. These plumes rise up into the upper part of the mantle as hot spots. When a plume rises, it can spread out and cover an area a few hundred miles across. A result of this process is volcanic activity.

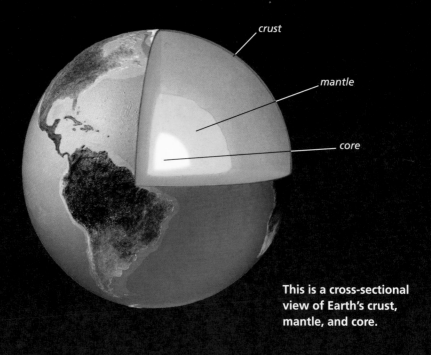

crust

mantle

core

This is a cross-sectional view of Earth's crust, mantle, and core.

200 million years ago

135 million years ago

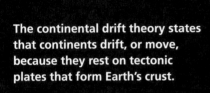

The continental drift theory states that continents drift, or move, because they rest on tectonic plates that form Earth's crust.

10 million years ago

   The theory of plate tectonics is based on the theory of continental drift. Proposed by Alfred Wegener in the early 1900s, this theory states that one huge continent, Pangaea, existed on Earth about 200–250 million years ago. After about 100 million years, streams of molten rock in the mantle caused Pangaea to split into pieces. These pieces eventually became the seven continents that exist on Earth today.

   Wegener supported his theory with observations about the shape of the Earth's continents. He noticed that the continents fit together like pieces in a puzzle. For example, the eastern edge of South America and the western edge of Africa seemed to fit so perfectly that they could have actually been joined at one time.

   Wegener also knew that certain types of rock had been discovered on more than one continent. The discovery of rock formations that extended over the current boundaries of South America and Africa strongly supported the idea that the continents were once joined.

As you read earlier, the movement of plates can cause collisions along boundaries. Sometimes, when two plates collide, the heavier plate is forced down into the mantle, forming what is called a subduction zone. When this happens, the Earth's crust sinks into the mantle. The rock along the lower edge of the plate is melted by molten rock, or magma. The magma rises, forcing its way through the lithosphere and the plate above it, and flows out as a volcano. Since many subduction zones exist in the Ring of Fire, it is a region of intense volcanic activity.

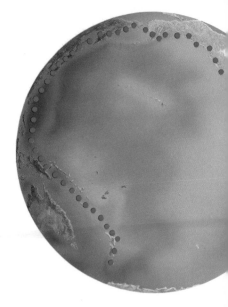

This view of Earth shows the Pacific Ocean. The dots indicate the Ring of Fire.

Many hot spots also exist within the Ring of Fire. Scientists believe that the Hawaiian Islands formed over a hot spot. The Pacific plate slid northwest and traveled over the hot spot. Magma rose up through the ocean floor and formed a volcanic island. As the plate continued to move, a magma eruption created another island.

The first islands formed, Kauai and Oahu, have no active volcanoes at this time. Currently the Big Island of Hawaii is above the hot spot. The active volcanoes there are Mauna Loa and Kilauea.

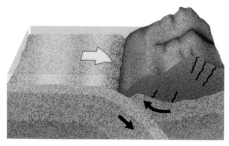

plates colliding

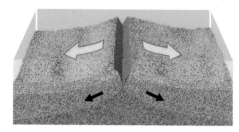

plates moving apart

The Kilauea volcano erupts at a vent known as Puu Oo. Within the cone is a crater enclosing a lava lake. Note the fountains of lava bursting forth from the lake.

Volcanoes

Volcanoes usually occur in areas where tectonic plates collide. The collision of plates causes Earth's crust to crack. Heat and pressure become so intense that parts of the mantle melt. Molten rock and hot gases are forced out through the cracks in the crust.

Volcanoes are classified as active, dormant, and extinct. An active volcano is one that could erupt at any time, even though it is not necessarily in the process of erupting. There are about 1,500 active volcanoes on Earth, with about fifty in the United States. A dormant volcano is one that has been inactive for a long period of time. Mount Pinatubo is a volcano in the Philippines, an island chain in the western Pacific Ocean. It was dormant for six centuries before it erupted in 1991. The huge eruption covered an area of 4,000 square kilometers with ash. An extinct volcano is one that shows no signs of erupting again.

Although dormant volcanoes are currently inactive, they may still continue to let off steam because of the magma that exists inside them. Dormant volcanoes may have craters, bowl-shaped areas that hold boiling lava. Lava is the name for magma that has erupted. Craters are formed by magma that is expelled through a vent and forms a lava lake. During dormant periods, the lava in the lake cools and hardens over the vent. When pressure builds up, the volcano may erupt again in a huge explosion.

Explosive Force

The girl in the photo uses a bottle of soda to model the process of a volcanic eruption. She shakes the bottle gently and then shakes it more vigorously. When she opens the bottle, the trapped gas, carbon dioxide, spurts out.

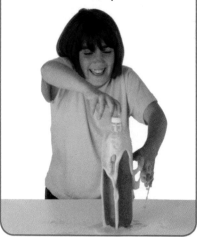

Inside a Volcano

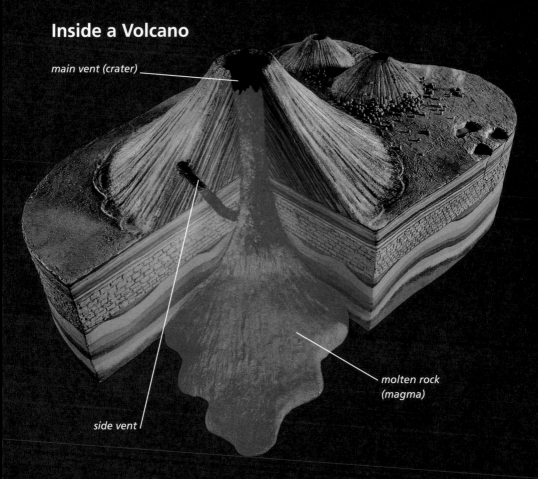

main vent (crater)

molten rock
(magma)

side vent

During a volcanic eruption, magma and hot gases from Earth's mantle flow up. They erupt through a vent, or hole, in the crust. They also may erupt through a vent at the side of the volcano.

Different types of volcanoes produce different types of eruptions. In less-violent eruptions, streams of lava flow gently through vents in the volcano. Runny lava can travel great distances before it solidifies and stops. When the lava is viscous, or thick and sticky, more violent eruptions may take place. Lava fragments, hot rocks, ash, and dust may be shot out over the surrounding area. A layer of ash several feet thick may cover the area. In addition, volcanic ash can be suspended in air for some time.

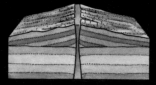

fissure volcano

In a fissure volcano, lava erupts from a long crack in Earth's surface. Lava may erupt from several places along the crack.

shield volcano

Shield volcanoes erupt into broad, flat mounds. Basalt lava pours from many side vents.

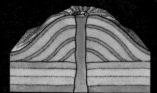

dome volcano

Dome volcanoes erupt viscous lava, which slowly builds up over the vent and forms a dome.

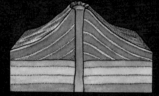

cinder cone volcano

Hard fragments of lava, ash, and volcanic gases erupt from cinder cone volcanoes. The volcanic material erupts from a main vent and forms a cone shape.

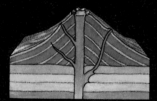

composite volcano

These symmetrical volcanoes usually have steep sides and cratered summits.

caldera volcano

When a volcano is so violent that it collapses in on itself, a caldera, a large bowl shape, is formed.

When an extremely forceful volcanic eruption takes place, it can actually destroy the volcano. The explosion causes the sides of the crater to collapse and form a caldera—a wide bowl-shaped hole more than a kilometer wide. An example is Mount Mazama in southwestern Oregon. When it erupted over 6,000 years ago, it left a caldera more than nine kilometers wide and about two kilometers deep. The caldera that was formed is now known as Crater Lake.

Volcanic eruptions produce different types of lava. One type, *aa*, is lava that cools quickly and hardens into rough chunks of rock. Another type, *pahoehoe*, is thin lava that cools more slowly and hardens into smooth, ropy pieces. Pumice is lava that cools and hardens into a lightweight rock with many air bubbles in it. Pumice can be either *aa* or *pahoehoe*.

aa

pahoehoe

Cerro Azul is a shield volcano located in the Galapagos Islands. The volcano has erupted eight times, sometimes endangering the nesting zones of giant tortoises. The caldera is small in diameter, but very deep.

Mount St. Helens erupted on May 18, 1980, spewing hot rocks, dust, and gases.

Several famous volcanoes exist around the Ring of Fire. Mount Paricutin, in Mexico, is an example of a cinder cone volcano. Paricutin first erupted in 1943, and the eruption continued for about eight more years. Eruptions of gases and molten lava fell back around the vent and built up the cone to 1,100 feet. The final eruption left a crater shaped like a funnel at the top of the cinder cone. Lava continued to flow out onto the surface surrounding the cone.

Over a period of nine years, Paricutin covered an area of about 100 square miles with ash and destroyed the town of San Juan. During this time, geologists around the world were able to observe Paricutin and study its development.

Mount St. Helens had been inactive for approximately 123 years. In 1978, scientists studying the volcano predicted that it would erupt in the next ten years. In March of 1980, small explosions began, with some ash and smoke coming out of the vent. In April the north side began to bulge out, and in May the devastating eruption occurred. The volcano ejected pieces of rocks, ash, and a cloud of gases. In 1982, the area became Mount St. Helens National Volcanic Monument. Visitors at the site can learn all about volcanoes.

Mount Pinatubo, in the Philippines, erupted on June 15, 1991. Three days earlier, a cloud of volcanic ash and gas rose up above the mountain. People in the surrounding area felt the ground tremble and noticed steam spurting from cracks in the rocks. Scientists predicted the eruption and warned people to leave the area. About 300 people were killed, but at least 5,000 lives were saved because of early warning.

Mount Fuji is a composite volcano. Its first eruption occurred at least 3,000 years ago. The most recent eruption was in 1707, when ash and huge pieces of rock were ejected. In 2000, tremors occurred in the area, and in 2003, steam was detected coming from vents on the northeastern side.

A thick coat of ash covered the landscape after Pinatubo erupted.

Mount Fuji, the highest mountain in Japan, has a large, circular crater at the summit.

Earthquakes

Locations that are likely to have volcanic activity are also likely to have earthquake activity. As tectonic plates slide, scrape, and collide, the movement creates cracks in the crust. These cracks are called faults. Over time, pressure in the crust builds until it can't be contained any longer. Finally, the rock splits along the fault, and an earthquake occurs.

Since most faults exist where plate boundaries collide, most earthquakes happen where two or more plate boundaries meet. However, faults can be located anywhere in the crust. Whenever there is movement along a fault, an earthquake happens. Some faults are close to the surface, while others are deep in the crust. Earthquakes that occur close to the surface are more likely to be felt and to do the most damage. Some earthquakes originate within the upper mantle.

Buildings topple over.

The street collapses.

This model of a street illustrates the damage that an earthquake can cause.

Each earthquake has a focus, which is the place where it begins underground. Directly above the focus, on the surface, is its epicenter. Energy moves away from the focus in the form of seismic, or shock, waves. Different types of seismic waves produce the earthquake's initial jolt, shake the ground in all directions, or produce a rolling, wavelike motion.

Seismologists, scientists who study earthquakes, measure seismic waves and determine the magnitude, or size, of an earthquake. They use this information to give each earthquake a number rating on the Richter scale. The scale begins at zero and increases by one number at a time. However, the amount of ground movement is ten times the amount of the previous number. While the Richter scale has no upper limit, the largest earthquakes recorded on the scale have had a magnitude of approximately 8.9.

Description	Richter Magnitudes	Earthquake Effects	Average Annually
Micro	Less than 2.0	Microearthquakes, not felt	About 8,000 per day
Very minor	2.0–2.9	Generally not felt, but recorded	About 1,000 per day
Minor	3.0–3.9	Often felt, but rarely cause damage	49,000 (estimated)
Light	4.0–4.9	Shaking of indoor items, rattling noises	6,200 (estimated)
Moderate	5.0–5.9	Can cause major damage to poorly constructed buildings over small regions	800
Strong	6.0–6.9	Can be destructive in areas up to one hundred miles across	120
Major	7.0–7.9	Can cause serious damage over larger areas	18
Great	8.0 or greater	Can cause serious damages in areas hundreds of miles across	1

Locations along the Ring of Fire are especially inclined to earthquake activity. The Pacific plate, almost 9,000 miles wide, is the largest tectonic plate. On its eastern boundary, it meets the North American plate. The San Andreas fault is located at the junction of these two plates. The fault is 10 miles deep and stretches north along the coast of California for about 750 miles. About twenty major earthquakes occurred along the San Andreas fault in the twentieth century.

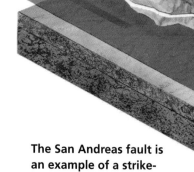

The San Andreas fault is an example of a strike-slip fault. The fault runs vertically through rock. Rock on one side slips and scrapes past the other.

The 1989 earthquake in San Francisco caused buildings to collapse.

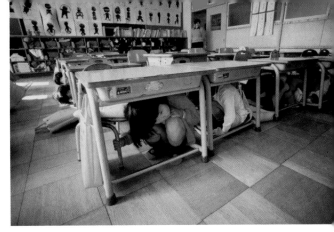

Students in Japan practice regular earthquake drills.

The city of San Francisco is located near the fault line and has been the site of major earthquakes. In 1906 a magnitude 8.3 earthquake, known as the Great San Francisco Earthquake, hit the city in the early morning hours. Buildings crumbled into the streets, gas pipes broke, and the city's main water pipelines broke. Dozens of fires broke out, but without water, firefighters couldn't put them out. The fires raged through the city for three days. In the end, about 90 percent of the total damage was due to fire.

The United States Geological Survey predicted that a moderate-to-large earthquake would hit San Francisco between 1988 and 2018. In October 1989 their prediction proved to be correct when an earthquake shook the city again. This earthquake occurred just before a World Series game was to be played in Candlestick Park. Measuring 7.1 on the Richter scale, the earthquake was responsible for the destruction of 100,000 buildings and the collapse of a section of the San Francisco Bay Bridge.

Other devastating earthquakes have occurred in locations along the Ring of Fire, such as Kobe, Japan; Northridge, California; and Anchorage, Alaska. Because the likelihood of earthquake activity is so great in this region, schoolchildren living there routinely perform earthquake drills in school. Schools conduct the drills so that students will know what to do if an earthquake occurs.

Research

Scientists who specialize in the study of volcanoes are called volcanologists. Volcanologists monitor volcanic and earthquake activity in order to make more accurate predictions and save more lives. Their work involves a variety of research activities. They may climb mountains to search through a lava flow or crawl into craters to collect samples of rock and volcanic gases. By analyzing the gases, they can sometimes predict changes in a volcano's activity.

Many volcanologists work for the U.S. Geological Survey. This government agency maintains five observatories in the United States. The scientists at the location in Hawaii predict, monitor, and study the activity of the Kilauea and Mauna Loa volcanoes. At the site in Washington State, scientists monitor Mount St. Helens and other volcanoes in the Cascade Mountain range. In Alaska, geologists from the agency and the University of Alaska monitor the twenty active volcanoes there and eighty others in the North Pacific.

Volcanologists use special types of equipment and tools in their research. Equipment includes heat suits and gloves to protect them when they observe active volcanoes, and helmets and face masks to protect them from falling rocks, dust, and poisonous gases. They use special thermometers called thermocouples to record the temperature of lava flows.

Volcanologists expect more volcanic and earthquake activity to occur in the Ring of Fire. Hopefully, they will be able to predict it in time to save lives.

The zigzag lines recorded on this seismogram indicate the size of an earthquake.

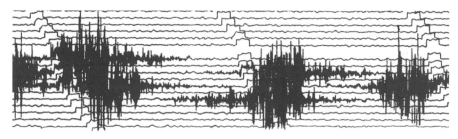

A volcanologist wears a special heat suit while observing a lava eruption.

Glossary

caldera   a large depression formed when a volcanic crater collapses

cinder cone   a volcano formed from ash and loose bits of rock from an explosive volcanic eruption

epicenter   the point on Earth's surface that lies directly above the focus of an earthquake

fissure   a jagged crack in Earth's crust, caused by earthquakes, volcanic activity, and plate movements

magma   hot liquid rock and gases inside Earth

magnitude   a measurement of the size of an earthquake based on the energy released and the size of the seismic waves created

volcanologists   scientists who study volcanoes